Published by
Orbis Publishing Ltd
Griffin House
161 Hammersmith Road
London W6 8SD

Translation by Beatrice Vincenzini
Calligraphy by Francesca Cassavetti

Printed by Officine Grafiche de Agostini,
Novara, Italy

KLAUS THE GNOME PRESENTS

Around the World
with the
GNOMES

Volume 46

ORBIS PUBLISHING

A blanket of snow

Pink clouds hang in the winter sky – warning gnomes that the dawn is near and that they should be returning to their beds. But when the ground is white with snow and icicles glisten by the banks of the stream, no gnome ever feels like going home.

Grassy hillocks, where we gather flowers and dew at other times of the year, suddenly become exciting ski-runs; snowy branches hang low to the ground, creating challenging assault courses; and ponds freeze over to form miniature ice-rinks.

But despite this natural playground, we are sometimes a bit lonely in wintertime. Many of our bird and animal friends have migrated to warmer climates. The woods are silent and we miss the chattering creatures that we used to meet on our travels. But wait, not all the animals have left the woods...

Tucked away beneath the ground, under stones and inside trees, is a secret store of sleeping animals. Many are in hibernation, but others simply prefer to spend their time curled up in warm burrows, out of the winter cold.

The dormouse has made a nest in a hollow tree. He is the sleepy-head of the woods — when spring arrives it is always hard to wake him up.

It must be cold because even the lizard is hiding under a stone.

In winter toads stay in their holes.

The tortoise has a protective covering, but he still feels the cold. Sleeping in an underground den is the best solution.

The Campas

The Campas live in a place known as the Gran Pajonal. It is one of the most inaccessible areas of Peru. The high mountains of the Andes, the thick forests of the Amazonian basin and unnavigable rivers have protected this small group of people from the interference of other settlers.

Life isn't easy for the few thousand Campa who still follow the traditional ways of their ancestors. Before they can build a village or grow any crops, these people must create a clearing in the forest. They do this by cutting down the trees and setting light to the remaining tree trunks and stubble.

The houses which they build are very plain. They have no walls, only poles at the four corners which hold up the roof. Rush mats cover the floor and a few possessions are arranged around the sleeping area.

The Campa grow cassava, plantains (large bananas) and sugar cane in their fields. The women crush and cook them ready for eating.

A hollowed-out tree trunk makes the ideal basin for preparing dyes from tree bark and plant roots.

The men do all the hunting and fishing for the tribe. Young boys help the women until they are old enough to join the men on their expeditions.

The biggest and the boldest

Many of the animals which live in the forests of South America are fascinating. The whole of the South American continent was once an island, cut off from North America. This meant that the animals which lived there developed in isolation from other animals.

The murky waters of the Amazonian rivers contain some of the largest creatures in the world: the arrau – the biggest fresh-water turtle; the arapaima – the longest and fattest inland fish; the capybara – the largest rodent; the anaconda – the mightiest snake; and the giant otter.

The other birds, animals and fish are just as extraordinary; for example, the only true flying fish. It is known as the hatchet fish because of the round axe-like shape of its body. Unlike other 'flying fish', the hatchet fish actually flaps its fins to fly, rather than flicking itself into the air with its tail. Another Amazonian fish is the piranha – one of the most feared fresh-water fish in the world.

The hoatzin is another unusual forest inhabitant. This ancient-looking bird builds a nest on a branch overhanging the river. It feeds on leaves and fruit, as well as grubs, insects and seeds, for which it forages on the forest floor. The chicks are even odder than their parents. For the first few weeks of life, they have two large claws at the front of each wing, which help them scramble around. This stops them falling into the water – although, unlike their parents, the chicks are able to swim.

Ogres aren't so 'orrible

The ogres of fairy tales are always wicked. Stories tell of hideous, grumpy creatures who live on nothing but human flesh. It is true that all the ogres which I have seen during my lifetime were ugly – certainly not the type to win a woodland beauty contest!

Sometimes ogres can be grumpy, too, but this is usually because they have been insulted or they haven't understood (all ogres are incredibly stupid). As for the idea of them eating human flesh, well, this is an exaggeration – they may eat a pig, goat or sheep, but never a person!

In fact, there are all sorts of stories about ogres. Some say that they live in gloomy castles on top of tall mountains, and trick their victims by re-directing signposts. Others say that, like witches, ogres can cast spells.

...But gnomes know different. Ogres live in woods and, despite their size, are usually harmless.

There are two references to ogres in *The Secret Book*. The first gives a brief description of what they look like (just in case we should happen to meet one on our travels). The second concerns an incident of great importance to the gnome community.

'A young ogre once lived in a forest near to a human village. One day while out chopping wood, his axe broke and he could chop no more fire-wood. But it was winter, and the ogre soon grew cold, so he decided to visit his neighbours in the village.

'His first stop was at the home of the village wood-cutter, who, on seeing the ogre, slammed the door in his face. Next he tried the baker and the miller, but each shut him out, without even a word of explanation.

'So, in a rage, the ogre went back to the forest and uprooted all the trees, one by one. The next morning when the villagers awoke they saw that the forest had disappeared, as if by magic. They soon realised what had happened and how mean they had been towards the young ogre.

'Their regret was too late, however, because the damage had been done: the ogre had been offended; many gnomes had lost their houses as the trees were uprooted.

'...And all over a few pieces of firewood!'

The sleepy-head of the woods

Dormice are well-known for their sleeping habits – remember the dormouse in *Alice in Wonderland*? He slept in a teapot, but most dormice prefer trees. The important point is that they sleep a lot!

As the leaves on the trees begin to curl up and turn brown, these furry creatures prepare themselves for a their long winter sleep. Searching by night, they eat more and more food as the colder months approach. By the time they hibernate, dormice look like little round balls of fluff.

During the summer, they live in abandoned birds' nests, hollow trees or tangled bushes. But as winter approaches, dormice become more choosy about their accommodation: the nest must face south and be in a safe place, away from predators.

This garden dormouse is snug and warm in his winter den. If the cold weather continues, he may stay there for as long as nine months.

The thin and scruffy creature which awakes in the springtime is very different to the fat and contented one which began the winter hibernation. All its fat reserves have been used up, and so the dormouse must eat lots of food to regain some weight – not that it minds!

All dormice are agile climbers, but Elizabeth, the edible dormouse, is better equipped than most – look at her bushy tail, it must be so helpful for balance. In fact, don't you think she looks like a squirrel? I am always mistaking these two animals, it's so embarrassing!

In Roman times, the rich regarded edible dormice as an especially tasty treat. They were kept in captivity and fed acorns and nuts to fatten them up before cooking. Elizabeth is very relieved that she didn't live in Roman times, even though she's fond of acorns and nuts!

Dormice are as fond of cherries as gnomes are, so we often meet them when we are out gathering cherries. They are real chatterboxes, though, and manage to eat and talk all at once.

During the summer, edible dormice often sleep in trees. Elizabeth is explaining how she once fell out of a tree while sleeping. It was four hours before she woke up and found herself in a bramble patch!

Edible or 'fat' dormice prefer to hibernate in hollows underground rather than in trees. Tree roots give ideal shelter. Once a dormouse has found the right spot, it will line its hollow with soft leaves and dry twigs, then lay in a stock of nuts and seeds for when it wakes up hungry.

Little Red Riding Hood
...and the gnome

'Once upon a time there was a little girl whose
name was Little Red Riding Hood, because she
used to wear a red cloak with a hood. One day,
her mother said to her: "Why don't you go to
visit your poor grandmother, who is ill in
bed, and take her this apple cake?" '

...And so begins the famous fairy tale.

Gnome parents also tell this story to their children,
but not without adding an extra character
– a gnome, of course.

Here is what they tell: 'As Little Red Riding Hood set off
to visit her granny, she was thinking about the warning
that her mother had given her. "Follow the long path
around the wood, straight to Granny's house. Whatever
you do, don't enter the wood, as there is a hungry wolf on
the prowl." But it was a hot day and the wood looked
cool and welcoming, so she set off between the
trees. Unknown to her, two pairs of eyes had
seen her entering – one belonged to the
wolf, and the other to a gnome.

'She wandered deeper and deeper into the wood, picking flowers to take to her ailing grandmother. Then, all of a sudden, she came face to face with the wolf. "Hello there," he said with a grin, "what's your name?" Little Red Riding Hood didn't know what to do, but she had been brought up well and felt it only polite to answer. "My name is Little Red Riding Hood, what's yours?" The wolf replied that his name was William and said how glad he was to meet such a well-mannered little girl in the wood. Little Red Riding Hood began to think that perhaps the wolf wasn't as wicked as her mother had warned, and so the two began to chat.

'Just as the wolf began to lick his lips and move closer to Little Red Riding Hood, the gnome who had been following her trail appeared. The wolf watched angrily as the gnome stepped up onto a tree stump between them.

'Looking at the wolf, the gnome demanded "What's going on here?" So Little Red Riding Hood told him how nice the wolf had been to her. The gnome knew otherwise, though, and quickly sent her on her way, explaining how first appearances can be deceptive.

Quietly, the wolf slunk off. But unknown to the gnome, he had already discovered where Little Red Riding Hood's granny lived. And the rest of the story you know!

Lighthouse gnomes

Wherever there are rocks beneath the surface of the sea, which
may cause a shipwreck, there is usually a lighthouse. And
wherever there is a lighthouse, you can be sure that there is a
Lighthouse gnome. He will be a shy, private individual, who
doesn't mind the isolation of his sea-bound home.

Lighthouse gnomes live a rugged life. They love the sea and craggy islands on which they live. They enjoy the noise of the waves crashing against the rocks and the sounds of the wind whistling around the lighthouse. Their friends are the sea birds: the seagulls, cormorants, gannets and terns. Occasionally a seal may rest for a while on the rocks or bob up and down close to the shore, shouting greetings to the gnome-keeper, or passing on a message from another gnome.

When the weather is bad, lighthouse gnomes may not receive a visitor for months on end. But their friends and relatives never forget them — parcels of food and gifts arrive regularly on the backs of travelling birds. This swallow has just sent down a package containing chestnut cookies, cream fudge and strawberry dew liqueur. What a feast!

When the weather is good, friends and relatives visit often. But when the wind is high and a storm is brewing, no gnome would dare risk a journey to this bleak location. The Lighthouse gnome is far too busy to receive visitors, anyway. The light must be tended and codes sent out to passing ships. If a fog has settled, then he must sound the fog horn, too.

But there is one great advantage to lighthouse life. The sunsets and sunrises are incomparable. In fact, the Lighthouse gnome wakes up a little earlier and goes to bed a little later than most other gnomes, just to see these wonderful spectacles.

The lighthouse stands on a small islet at the edge of the main island. After a storm, the gnome keeper rows his boat around the larger island to check that there are no injured birds or animals washed up on the beaches.

AN OXEN-POWERED SHIP

'An old lighthouse gnome drew a picture of this strange vessel. Whether he actually saw it from the top of his lighthouse, or thought up the idea himself, nobody knows. It looks as if it would work, though...

As the oxen walk round, they rotate the main axle. These, in turn, rotate the side wheels, which then dip their blades into the water and push the boat along. My only worry is that no one is standing at the tiller to steer it!'

Fruit juices

In summertime the fruit trees which we have planted in the wood begin to bear fruit. The cherries are ready first, then the apples and pears (which ripen towards the end of summer). Finally, we pick the grapes. These may not be ready until the end of October, but they are well worth waiting for.

When the harvest has been brought in, we usually sit down with a glass of refreshing fruit juice.

① Cherries are full of vitamin A, calcium and phosphorus. We use sweet cherries to make cherry juice as sour ones make our eyes water.

② The juice from the crushed fruit is poured into a large jar and chilled. A mixture of a few different flavours is the best.

③ Oranges and mandarines don't grow well in this country, but Mediterranean and Middle Eastern gnomes will often bring us one when they visit.

④ Apples provide us with vitamins A and C as well as lots of dietary fibre.

⑤ Young gnomes don't like carrot juice very much, even though it is good for them. I love to nibble a raw carrot, especially if it is a young tender one, picked fresh from the garden.

Pigs in the wild

Boars, or wild pigs, can live anywhere, but they prefer the woods. Here they can find their favourite woodland plants, as well as worms, insects, frogs, mice and other small animals.

The European wild boar is the largest of the species, standing up to 90 centimetres tall. It is easily recognisable by its dark brown, bristly hair and long snout with sharp tusks.

Male boars are solitary creatures, wandering the woods alone for most of the year. At breeding time they become more sociable – but only with the females; the males spend all their time fighting each other!

The female gives birth to up to 12 babies. She builds a snug nest of branches, plants and hay for her piglets, which are very small and vulnerable after the birth. They therefore remain huddled in the nest for the first 10 days, and stay with their mother until her next litter is born. Unlike their parents, the young boars have stripy coats, which look like pyjamas, to camouflage them in the woods.

Wild boars like to wallow in mud. But they don't do it just for fun, it is also a way of getting rid of any fleas, lice or ticks which are hiding in their thick coats. When the mud dries, creating a crust, the boar rubs itself against a tree trunk and the pests fall off with the mud.

A mother boar and her piglets may be joined by other families of females and babies. Sometimes as many as 100 boars gather together. These groups are known as 'sounders'. When one visits our wood, Juliana, Dany and I take a holiday, as the snuffling and stamping can be unbearable!

Boars are constantly hungry and they aren't fussy about what the eat, either. Sometimes they will wander into fields and dig up the roots and tubers planted there. As you can imagine, this makes them very unpopular with farmers. On the other hand, because they like to eat mice, rats and other animals which the farmer considers as pests, they are sometimes in his favour.

Once boars have found a hidden delicacy below ground, they will dig it out eagerly with their hooves and snout.

Despite their great bulk, wild boars are quite agile. Not only can they run fast, but they are also excellent swimmers. A wide river or large pond presents no problem to these creatures.

The chimaera

Greek legend tells of a terrible three-headed monster known
as the chimaera. Its head and front paws were those of a
lion; its hind legs, back and second head were those of a
goat; and its tail was a snake. If anyone dared to approach
this horrendous creature, it would send forth scorching
flames from its lion's mouth, while the serpent would raise
its hissing head and dart menacingly. If all this failed, the
goat's head would charge the intruder, using its sharp horns.

For many years, this monster ravaged the countries of Lycia. Until, one day, a Corinthian called Bellerophon was sent to the king of Lycia to be executed.

Not wishing to kill a warrior who was renowned for his bravery and honour, the king decided to set Bellerophon a challenge to decide his fate. The task was to kill the chimaera.

Bellerophon knew that the only chance he had of reaching the chimaera's den and achieving his goal was to fly on the back of Pegasus. But how could he catch and tame such a wild horse?

Upon advice, Bellerophon spent a night in the temple of Athene, the goddess of war. While he slept, Athene appeared to him in a dream and gave him a golden bridle, which remained after he awoke. Thus, he tamed Pegasus and the young warrior reached the chimaera's cave. When the creature rushed out at them, it was more fearsome than he had imagined.

Spitting fire, the creature hurled itself at Pegasus and Bellerophon. But Athene had also advised the warrior on how to kill the monster. Using a lead-tipped spear, he stabbed the chimaera between the gaping jaws of its lion's head. As the spear went down its throat, the flames melted the tip and the red-hot metal flowed down into the beast's body. It was killed instantly and Bellerophon returned victoriously to Lycia to wed the king's daughter.

FROM JULIANA'S DIARY

Here are two of my favourite
rhymes. They are very old, but
they still give useful advice.

A rhyme for chattering creatures:
'A wise old owl sat in an oak,
The more he heard the less he spoke;
The less he spoke, the more he heard.
Why aren't we all like that wise old bird?'

Advice for anyone saving up for
a holiday:
'Penny and penny
Stored up will be many;
Who will not save a penny
Shall never have many.'

Contents